The Pet Bath

by Nancy Leber and Amy Levin
Illustrated by Abby Carter

SCHOLASTIC

Meg gets a tub.

Kim gets suds.

2

Gus and Max get rags.

This is the pet bath.

"Here is my pup.

Can she get a bath?"

The pup gets in the tub.

She gets a bath.

"This is my big dog.

Can he get a bath?"

7

The big dog gets in the tub.

The pup and the big dog get a bath.

"This is my little dog.

Can she get a bath?"

The little dog gets in the tub.

The pup, the big dog, and the

little dog get a bath.

Pet Bath

The dogs are wet.

Meg, Kim, Gus, and Max are wet.

They are all wet!

Meg rubs the pup with thick rags.

Kim and Max rub the big dog
with thick rags.

Gus rubs the little dog

with thick rags.

Ben and Jess come.

"Here is our .

Can he get a bath?"

Look who gets a bath now!

My Words

* little	dog	Meg
* now	get	pet
* our	gets	rags
and	in	wet
big	Kim	
can	Max	

Uu

Gus	rub	tub
pup	suds	

th-/-th

thick	bath
this	with

*new high frequency words